D1096701

OFFICIALLY
WITHDRAWN

POPULAR LECTURES IN MATHEMATICS SERIES

EDITORS: I. N. SNEDDON AND M. STARK

Volume 5

THE RULER IN
GEOMETRICAL CONSTRUCTIONS

TITLES IN THE POPULAR LECTURES IN MATHEMATICS SERIES

THE RULER IN
GEOMETRICAL
CONSTRUCTIONS

by
A. S. SMOGORZHEVSKII

Translated from the Russian by
HALINA MOSS, B.Sc.

Translation Editor
IAN N. SNEDDON
Simson Professor of Mathematics
in the University of Glasgow

BLAISDELL PUBLISHING COMPANY
NEW YORK · LONDON
A DIVISION OF RANDOM HOUSE

SOLE DISTRIBUTORS IN THE UNITED STATES AND CANADA
Blaisdell Publishing Company
22 East 51st Street, New York 22, N.Y.

Copyright © 1961
PERGAMON PRESS LTD.

A translation of the original volume
Lineika v geometricheskikh postroyeniyakh
(Moscow, Gostekhteoretizdat, 1957)

Library of Congress Card Number: 61-11531

Printed in Great Britain by Pergamon Printing and Art Services Limited, London

68058
Fort Lewis College Library

C O N T E N T S

F O R E W O R D

The study of the constructive power of a ruler and compasses, that is of the set of problems soluble by means of these classical tools of geometric constructions (both together or each separately), was carried out fully only in the 19th century. Until then some mathematicians regarded the ruler and compasses as universal instruments, which, if used together, were capable of solving any construction problem. This point of view played a negative role in the history of geometry. It prompted a premeditated attempt to regard each problem on construction as soluble by means of a ruler and compasses and led to the misuse of enormous effort on the futile search for non-existing solutions; this happened, for instance, with problems on squaring the circle, trisecting an angle, duplication of the cube*.

The investigation of constructions carried out by means of a ruler alone was given a stimulus by the development of the theory of perspective and by the necessity of performing constructions over large portions of the earth's surface, where the application of compasses with a large opening is technically impossible, while the construction of straight lines is easily achieved by the use of surveying instruments.

In the present book the most typical construction problems, soluble by means of ruler alone, are considered.

---

*This was the way of stating the following problems:
   (1) Given the radius of a circle, to construct a square equal in area to the given circle.
   (2) To divide a given angle into three equal parts.
   (3) Given the edge of a cube, to construct the edge of a new cube, whose volume is twice that of the given cube.
It has been proved that the first and the third problems cannot be solved by means of a ruler and compasses, the second one being soluble by means of these instruments only in certain cases, for instance, when the given angle is a right angle.

Foreword

The cases when the effectiveness of the use of the ruler is enhanced by the use of a previously drawn definite auxiliary figure in the plane of construction (for example two parallel straight lines or two intersecting circles) are worthy of attention. Many of these cases are also considered by us.

In our presentation, we shall keep to the methods of synthetic geometry, i.e. we avoid the application of methods characteristic of arithmetic and algebra. We only permitted some minor deviations from this principle in some of the initial sections, motivated by the desire to simplify the presentation.

We should observe that the proofs of theorems and solutions of problems based on the application of methods of synthetic geometry are often distinguished by great elegance and originality; we hope that the reader will find in this book many examples confirming these words.

We draw the attention of the reader to Section 18, where it is shown that, using the ruler alone, it is impossible to construct the centres of two given non-concentric circles if these circles have no common point. It is well known, that 'proofs of impossibility' belong, mostly, to the class of difficult mathematical problems and are usually based on profound and difficult reasoning. We think, that the reader will be interested in the contents of the section mentioned above, where one such proof is to be found.

Part One

SOME THEOREMS OF SYNTHETIC AND PROJECTIVE GEOMETRY

1. INFINITELY DISTANT ELEMENTS OF A PLANE

We adopt the convention that any straight line (excluding the straight line at infinity, which will be discussed below) has one and only one point at infinity, which belongs also to all the lines parallel to the said straight line, and that the points at infinity of two straight lines, which intersect at a finite distance, are distinct.

On the basis of this convention we can state, that any two straight lines intersect, and they do so at one point only. If the lines are parallel, their point of intersection is at infinity.

Further, we shall call the collection of all the points at infinity in a plane 'a straight line at infinity'. Later, we shall see the significance of this definition.

The introduction of the idea of points at infinity and a straight line at infinity is suggested by the character of the problems which are investigated in this book. It will save us the necessity of complicating the formulation of a number of theorems, through pointing out exceptions which would occur if we did not use these ideas. On the other hand, they are directly connected with the operation of projection, which we shall now describe.

Suppose we are given a plane α with a point A in it and a point P outside α. Let the straight line PA intersect a plane β which does not pass through P, at the point B. Then B is called the <u>projection</u> of point A on to the plane β, the straight line PA is called the <u>projective ray</u>, the point P is called the <u>centre of projection,</u> β is called the plane of projection. Projection from one straight line on to another straight line can be considered in the same way, if these straight lines and the centre of projection lie on one plane.

If we are given a certain figure F in the plane α, then, if we project all its points from the centre P on to the plane β, we shall obtain in the plane β a figure Φ called

3

the projection of the figure F .

In particular the projection of a straight line will be a straight line.

It may turn out that the centre of projection P is a point at infinity. Then all the projective rays are parallel.

The projection procedure can be repeated several times. For example, having projected the figure Φ , as obtained above, from a centre Q not in the plane β , on to the plane γ , which does not pass through Q , we shall obtain a figure Ψ , which is also called a projection of the figure F . If the planes α and γ coincide, F and its projection Ψ will lie in the same plane.

Let us examine one special case. Suppose two parallel lines l and m (Fig. 1) are given in the plane α . The plane λ , which contains l and the centre of projection P, contains also all the rays projecting the points of the straight line l . The intersection l' of this plane with the plane β is

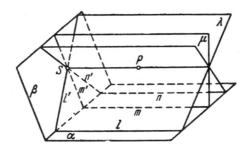

Fig. 1

the projection of l on to β . Similarly, the intersection m' of the plane β with the plane μ , which contains m and P , is the projection of the straight line m on to the plane β .

If the planes α and β are not parallel and the centre of projection P lies at a finite distance, the straight lines l' and m' intersect at a certain point S , while PS is parallel to α . If one more straight line n , parallel to the straight lines l and m is given in the plane α , then its

projection *n'* on to the plane β will also pass through the
point *S* .

It is natural to regard the point *S* as the projection of
the point at infinity common to the straight lines *l*, *m* and
n . Speaking more strictly, we have introduced the idea of
points at infinity for the very reason, that without it,
when considering the straight lines *l'*, *m'* and *n'* , as projections of the straight lines *l*, *m* and *n* we should have been
forced to exclude from them the point *S* in so far as it would
have had no prototype in the plane *α* .

It is not hard to conclude that the projection of the collection of all the points at infinity of the plane *α* on to
the plane β will be that straight line in the plane β , which
passes through the point *S* , parallel to the plane *α* ; hence
it is clear, why we have assigned this collection of points
to the category of straight lines, calling it the straight
line at infinity.

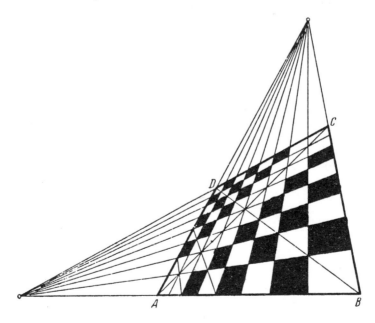

Fig. 2

On the basis of these considerations it is easy, for instance, to construct the projection of a chess-board, if the projection of its contour *ABCD* is given (Fig. 2).

Let us note, that parallel straight lines, in general, seem to us to converge in perspective; they are depicted in this way in pictures and drawings (for instance, Fig. 3).

Fig. 3

The study of projective properties of geometric figures, that is the properties which do not change on projection, is called projective geometry. Some theorems of projective geometry will be presented in this book.

In conclusion, we note that on occasion we shall consider a straight line as a circle of an infinitely large radius and centre at infinity on the perpendicular to that line.

2. INVERSE WITH RESPECT TO A CIRCLE

In this and the following two sections we shall discuss certain theorems relating circles; these theorems play an auxiliary part in our exposition.

Suppose we are given a circle x of radius r and centre K, and a point A other than K. On the ray KA let us select a point A' in such a way, that the product of the segments KA and KA' equals the square of the radius of the circle x :

$$KA \cdot KA' = r^2. \tag{1}$$

We then say that the points A and A' are inverse with respect to the circle x .

If one of the points A, A' lies outside the circle x , then the other one lies inside x , and <u>vice versa</u>; for example, from the inequality $KA' < r$ and condition (1), we conclude that $KA > r$. If either the point A or the point A' lies on the circle x then A and A' coincide.

Let us examine Fig. 4, where AB is a tangent to the circle x , BA' is a perpendicular to KA . Since the triangle KAB is

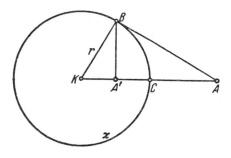

Fig. 4

7

a right-angled one, then

$$KA \cdot KA' = KB^2 = r^2,$$

and it follows that A and A' are inverse points with respect to $\varkappa$. Hence we have a method for constructing the point A' when we are given the point A , and the point A when we are given the point A' .

Let the segment AA' intersect the circle $\varkappa$ at the point C and let $A'C = a$, $CA = b$. Then $KA' = r - a$, $KA = r + b$. On the strength of (1) we shall have

$$(r + b)(r - a) = r^2,$$

Hence

$$b - a = \frac{ab}{r}. \tag{2}$$

If, keeping points C and A fixed, we increase r indefinitely, then in the limit, the circle $\varkappa$ will become a straight line, CD, perpendicular to CA, at the same time we get from (2):

$$b = a,$$

therefore the points A and A' are distributed symmetrically with respect to the straight line CD. Thus, in the limiting case, the property of being inverse with respect to a circle changes into symmetry with respect to a straight line*.

T h e o r e m   1. <u>If a circle λ passes through two distinct points A and A' inverse with respect to a circle $\varkappa$, then the circles $\varkappa$ and λ are mutually orthogonal.</u>

Two circles are called mutually orthogonal if they intersect at right angles, that is the tangents to the circles at their points of intersection (or, which is the same thing, their radii at that point) are mutually perpendicular**.

Let K and L be the centres of circles $\varkappa$ and λ , and P one of their points of intersection (Fig. 5). Since KP is a radius of the circle $\varkappa$, the equation (1) takes the form

---

*This explains why in Russian the points A, A' are called 'symmetrical' with respect to the circle (<u>editor</u>).
**If one of two orthogonal circles degenerates into a straight line, then that line passes through the centre of the other circle, which is easily verified.

$KA \cdot KA' = KP^2$. Hence we conclude, taking into account the theorem about the product of a secant to a circle and the

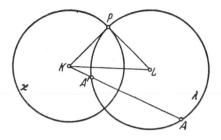

Fig. 5

part of it outside the circle, that KP is a tangent to the circle λ , therefore, radii KP and LP of the given circles are mutually perpendicular and these circles are mutually orthogonal.

T h e o r e m   2. <u>If the circles $\varkappa$ and λ are mutually orthogonal, then the straight line passing through the centre K of the circle $\varkappa$ and intersecting the circle λ, intersects it at points which are inverse with respect to $\varkappa$.</u>

We shall use Fig. 5, regarding the circles $\varkappa$ and λ as mutually orthogonal. Hence KP is a tangent to the circle λ . Let the straight line, passing through K , intersect λ at points A and A' . Then

$$KA \cdot KA' = KP^2.$$

Since the product of the segments KA and KA' equals the square of the radius KP of the circle $\varkappa$, then the points A and A' are inverse with respect to $\varkappa$, which is the required proof.

3. THE POWER OF A POINT WITH RESPECT TO A CIRCLE.
THE RADICAL AXIS OF TWO CIRCLES. THE
RADICAL CENTRE OF THREE CIRCLES

Suppose that we are given a circle x of radius r with a centre K and a point A situated at a distance d from K . The quantity

$$\sigma = d^2 - r^2 \qquad (1)$$

is called the <u>power of the point</u> A with respect to the circle x .

Let us investigate the following cases.

(1) A lies outside x . Then $d > r$, $\sigma > 0$.

In this case the quantity σ is equal to the square of the tangent from A to x , or, which is the same, to the product of the distances from A to the circle along any secant through A .

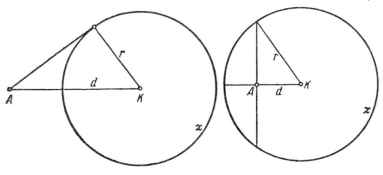

Fig. 6   Fig. 7

(2) A lies on x . Then $d = r$, $\sigma = 0$.

(3) A lies inside x . Then $d < r$, $\sigma < 0$. In this case

10

the quantity σ equals the square of half the smallest chord of the circle κ which passes through A , taken with a negative sign, or, which is the same thing, the product of the segments into which any chord passing through A is divided by A , taken with a negative sign (Fig. 7).

L e m m a. If the difference of the squares of the distances of a point M from two given points A and B is a constant quantity then the locus τ of the point M is a straight line perpendicular to the straight line AB.

Let a point N of the straight line AB and a point M outside this straight line both lie on the locus τ. Let us denote the lengths of the segments AB and AN by a and x respectively. According to the condition

$$AM^2 - BM^2 = c, \qquad (2)$$

where c is a given constant and

$$x^2 - (a - x)^2 = c.$$

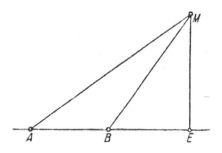

Fig. 8

From the latter equation we find

$$x = \frac{a^2 + c}{2a}.$$

Hence we conclude, that one and only one point of the locus τ lies on the straight line AB.

We now construct ME perpendicular to AB (Fig. 8). Then

$$AM^2 - AE^2 = EM^2 = BM^2 - BE^2.$$

Therefore

$$AM^2 - BM^2 = AE^2 - BE^2.$$

Using this and equation (2) above we have

$$AE^2 - BE^2 = c,$$

and this means that the points E and N coincide. Therefore τ is the perpendicular to the straight line AB drawn through the point N, which is what was to be proved.

T h e o r e m   3. <u>The locus of the point, whose powers with respect to two given circles are equal, is a straight line perpendicular to the line of centres of these circles.</u>

Let r_1 and r_2 be the radii of the given circles, d_1 and d_2 the distances of a point on the locus from their centres. Then, on the strength of (1)

$$d_1^2 - r_1^2 = d_2^2 - r_2^2.$$

Hence

$$d_1^2 - d_2^2 = r_1^2 - r_2^2. \tag{3}$$

When we apply the lemma, that has been proved above, to this equation with a constant right hand side, we convince ourselves of the truth of Theorem 3.

The locus discussed above is called the <u>radical axis</u> of two given circles.

The radical axis of two intersecting circles passes through their points of intersection, since the power of each of these points with respect to each of the given circles equals zero.

The radical axis of two circles just touching each other is their common tangent at their common point.

If two circles have no common point, then neither of the circles has a common point with the radical axis, otherwise both given circles would pass through that point.

T h e o r e m   4. <u>The radical axis of circles µ and ν</u>
(excluding their common chord, if they intersect) is the
locus of the centres of circles orthogonal to µ and ν .

Let us take a point P , outside the circles µ and ν and on
their radical axis (Fig. 9). The tangents from P to µ and ν
are equal as a consequence of the equality of the powers of
point P with respect to the given circles. Let PQ be one of

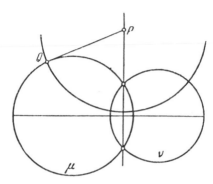

Fig. 9

these tangents. Evidently, the circle of radius PQ and
centre P is orthogonal to the circles µ and ν . On the
other hand, the tangents to µ and ν from the centre M of any
circle orthogonal to µ and ν are equal to the radius of that
circle; it follows that the powers of the point M with respect to µ and ν are equal, and M lies on the radical axis
of the given circles.

If circles µ and ν have a common centre N then the circles
orthogonal to them degenerate into straight lines passing
through N , and since the 'centre' of a straight line is a
point at infinity (Section 1), then Theorem 4 gives us reason to state that a straight line at infinity should be regarded as the radical axis of two concentric circles. It
is also easy to ascertain that none of the points situated
within finite distance can lie on the radical axis of two
concentric circles; indeed, for such a point, the left hand
side of the equation (3) would turn into zero, while the
right hand side would remain distinct from zero.

T h e o r e m   5. <u>The radical axes of three circles
taken two at a time, either intersect at a point called the</u>

<u>radical centre of these circles, or they coincide.</u>

Indeed, the common point of two radical axes has the same power with respect to each of the three circles, therefore it belongs also to the third radical axis. Hence it follows, in particular, that in the case when two radical axes coincide, the third one coincides with them, i.e. the three given circles have a common radical axis.

If the centres of three circles lie in one straight line, then their radical axes are parallel and, therefore, either intersect at a point at infinity, or coincide.

4. PENCILS OF STRAIGHT LINES AND COAXIAL CIRCLES

A pencil of straight lines is the name given to a collection of straight lines in a plane, all passing through one point - the vertex of the pencil. It is obvious that one and only one straight line of the pencil passes through any point in the plane other than the vertex of the pencil.

A coaxial system of circles is the name given to a collection of circles having a common radical axis, called the radical axis of the system.

In particular a collection of circles concentric to a given circle form a coaxial system whose radical axis is at infinity, and every point of the plane has one of these circles passing through it (their common centre represents a circle, which has shrunk to a point).

If we drop a perpendicular from the centre of one of two non-concentric circles on to their radical axis, it will pass through the centre of the second of these circles (Theorem 3). Hence, we conclude that coaxial circles have a common line of centres.

It follows from Theorem 4 that a circle which is orthogonal to two of the coaxial circles is also orthogonal to every circle of the system. Two circles μ and ν always define a system of coaxial circles.

We shall show how to draw a circle of this system through an arbitrary point P in the plane not belonging to either of the given circles or their radical axis. We shall examine these cases, taking the given circles as non-concentric.

(1) The circles μ and ν intersect at points A and B. The required circle will pass through the points A, B and P. Its centre lies on the line of centres of circles μ and ν, which is the perpendicular bisector* of the segment AB.

*The perpendicular bisector of a segment is the perpendicular to the segment at its midpoint.

15

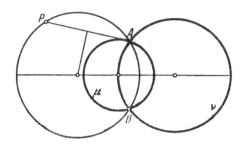

Fig. 10

In this case the system is called <u>elliptical</u>. All circles
of an elliptical coaxial system pass through the points of
intersection of two circles of this system (Fig. 10).

(2) The circles μ and ν touch at point C . The required
circle touches the given circles at the point C . Its centre
will be the point of intersection of the perpendicular bisecto:

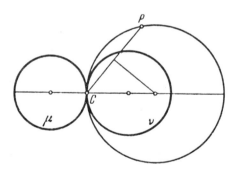

Fig. 11

of the segment CP with the line of centres of circles μ and
ν . Such a system is called <u>parabolic</u> (Fig. 11).

(3) The circles μ and ν have no common point. We construct
the circle κ , orthogonal to μ and ν , and the point P′ inverse to P with respect to κ (Fig. 12). The centre of the

required circle ξ will be the point of intersection of the perpendicular bisector of the segment PP′ with the line of centres
of the circles μ and ν . Indeed, on the strength of Theorem
1, the circle ξ is orthogonal to the circle x , therefore
tangents from the centre K of circle x to the circles μ, ν
and ξ are all equal.

If points P and P′ coincide, then the tangent from P to x
will play the part of the perpendicular bisector of the segment
PP′ . If P is the point of intersection of the circle x
with the line of centres of circles μ and ν , then the circle
ξ degenerates into the point P .

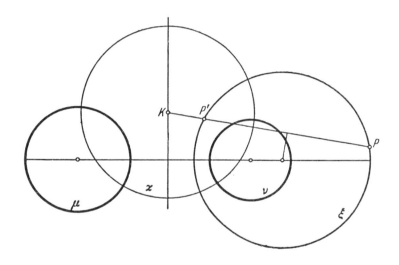

Fig. 12

In this case the system of coaxial circles is called hyperbolic. In a hyperbolic system no two circles have a common
point.

5. CROSS-RATIO

Let us consider a segment AB and a point C on the straight line l , and also a point P not on the straight line (Fig. 13). Let us denote the straight lines PA, PB, PC by a, b, c respectively, the angles PAB and PBA by α and β , the angle APB by (a, b) and so on.

Using the sine formula we get:

$$AC = CP \frac{\sin(a, c)}{\sin \alpha}, \qquad CB = CP \frac{\sin(c, b)}{\sin \beta}.$$

Hence

$$\frac{AC}{CB} = \frac{\sin(a, c)}{\sin(c, b)} \cdot \frac{\sin \beta}{\sin \alpha}. \tag{1}$$

When calculating the ratio $AC:CB$ according to formula (1) the direction of segments and angles must be taken into account. We shall ascribe to two segments the same sign if their direction is the same and different sign if their direction is opposite of each other. A similar agreement is introduced for angles. On the strength of this $AC:CB > 0$ if C lies between A and B and $AC:CB < 0$ if C lies on the straight line outside of the segment AB .

Let us consider one more point D of the straight line l and the straight line PD which we shall denote by d . By analogy to the equation (1) we obtain

$$\frac{AD}{DB} = \frac{\sin(a, d)}{\sin(d, b)} \cdot \frac{\sin \beta}{\sin \alpha}. \tag{2}$$

Let us introduce the following notation

$$(ABCD) = \frac{AC}{CB} : \frac{AD}{DB},$$

$$(abcd) = \frac{\sin(a, c)}{\sin(c, b)} : \frac{\sin(a, d)}{\sin(d, b)}.$$

The quantity $(ABCD)$ is called the <u>cross-ratio</u> of the four points

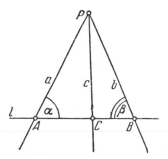

Fig. 13

A, B, C and D of the straight line. The quantity (abcd) is called the cross-ratio of the four straight lines a, b, c, d of the pencil. Cross-ratio is also known as <u>anharmonic ratio</u>.

From (1) and (2) we have the following equation:

$$(ABCD) = (abcd). \tag{3}$$

Let us draw a straight line l' other than l, not passing through P, and let us denote its points of intersection with a, b, c and d respectively by A', B', C' and D' (Fig. 14); obviously, these points can be considered as projections of points A, B, C, D on the line l' from the centre P. By analogy with the equation (3) we have

$$(A'B'C'D') = (abcd).$$

Hence and from (3) we get

$$(A'B'C'D') = (ABCD).$$

The following theorems are derived from what was said above.

T h e o r e m   6. <u>If the four straight lines of a pencil are intersected by a fifth straight line, then the cross-ratio of the four given straight lines equals the cross-ratio of the corresponding points of intersection.</u>

T h e o r e m   7. <u>The operation of projection does not change the value of the cross-ratio of four points of a</u>

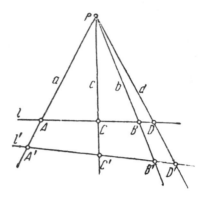

Fig. 14

straight line.

T h e o r e m   8. If in the cross-ratio $(ABCD)$ the points
A and B (or C and D) are inter-changed then the cross-ratio
takes the reciprocal value.

Indeed

$$(BACD) = \frac{BC}{CA} \cdot \frac{BD}{DA} = \frac{CB}{AC} \cdot \frac{DB}{AD} = \frac{1}{(ABCD)};$$

$$(ABDC) = \frac{AD}{DB} \cdot \frac{AC}{CB} = \frac{1}{(ABCD)} \ .$$

Finally, we shall note that the cross-ratio of four distinct points cannot equal unity. Indeed, if

$$(ABCD) = \frac{AC}{CB} \cdot \frac{AD}{DB} = 1,$$

then

$$\frac{AC}{CB} = \frac{AD}{DB}.$$

Hence, it follows, that if A and B are distinct points,
the points C and D coincide, therefore, our proposition is
true.

6. THE HARMONIC DISTRIBUTION OF FOUR POINTS ON A STRAIGHT LINE, AND FOUR STRAIGHT LINES OF A PENCIL

We shall say, that a pair of points C and D of a straight line divides a pair of points A, B of the same straight line harmonically, if the cross ratio $(ABCD)$ of these points equals -1:

$$(ABCD) = -1. \tag{1}$$

This means that the points C and D divide the segment AB in ratios whose absolute values are equal, one of the points dividing it internally, and the other one externally. Hence we have immediately:

T h e o r e m 9. In any triangle PQR, the pair of points of intersection of the straight line PQ with the bisectors of the angle at the vertex R and its complementary angle divides harmonically the pair of points P, Q.

If the condition (1) is fulfilled, then it is also said, that the points A, B; C, D of a straight line form a harmonic range, and the point D is called the fourth harmonic point to the points A, B; C. We draw attention to the use of punctuation marks in this notation; a semicolon separates the points of one pair from the points (or point of the second pair.

A similar terminology is used in connexion with the four straight lines a, b, c, d of a pencil, if

$$(abcd) = -1.$$

T h e o r e m 10. If a pair of points C, D divide harmonically the pair of points A, B, then the pair A, B divides harmonically the pair C, D also.

Indeed

$$(CDAB) = \frac{CA}{AD} : \frac{CB}{BD} = \frac{AC}{AD} : \frac{CB}{DB} = \frac{AC}{CB} : \frac{AD}{DB} = (ABCD) = -1.$$

T h e o r e m   11. <u>If the points A and A' are inverse with</u>
<u>respect to the circle x and the straight line AA' intersects</u>
<u>the circle x at points M and N , then the points A, A'; M, N</u>
<u>form a harmonic range.</u>

Let the point A lie outside of the circle x (Fig. 15).
Let us draw tangents AB and AC from A to x and let us construct the straight lines BC, BM, BN . Since the straight

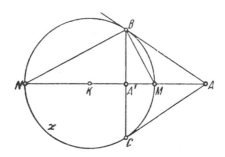

Fig. 15

line AA' passes through the centre of circles x , BC intersects
it at the point A' (Fig. 4).

$\angle ABM = \angle BNM$ as the angle between a tangent and a chord
is equal to the angle in the alternate segment. $\angle BNM =$
$\angle MBC$, each being the complement of $\angle NBC$. Thus $\angle ABM =$
$\angle MBC$. The straight line BM is therefore the bisector of
the angle B in the triangle ABA' and the straight line BN,
perpendicular to BM, is the bisector of the angle complementary to B. Therefore, on the strength of Theorem 9,
the points A, A'; M, N form a harmonic range.

Theorem 11 leads to a simple method of constructing the
fourth harmonic point D to three given points A, B; C, , lying
on one straight line: Using the segment AB as a diameter,
we describe the circle λ and we construct the point D , inverse to C with respect to λ . If the point C is the mid-
point of the segment AB , then, as is seen from this construction, D is a point at infinity.

In Section 11 we shall show, that it is possible to construct the fourth harmonic point by means of a ruler alone.

7. THE HARMONIC PROPERTIES OF A COMPLETE QUADRANGLE

The theorems that will be proved in this chapter are of great importance for understanding the later discussion; we shall make use of them in solving many construction problems.

A complete quadrangle is the name given to a figure consisting of four points - the vertices of the quadrangle no three of which lie on one straight line (A, B, C, D in Fig. 16) and six straight lines, joining these points in pairs - the sides of the quadrangle.

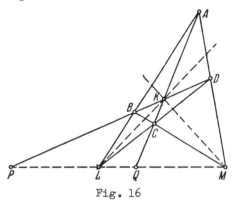

Fig. 16

The sides of a complete quadrangle intersect (apart from the vertices) in three more points (K, L, M in the figure). The straight lines KL, LM, MK are called the diagonals of the complete quadrangle.

T h e o r e m   12. Each pair of diagonals of a complete quadrilateral divides harmonically the pair of its sides which pass through the point of intersection of these diagonals.

Let the straight lines BD and AC intersect the diagonal LM of the complete quadrangle ABCD in the points P and Q (see Fig. 16). The points L, M, P and Q are respectively the projections of points B, D, P, K of the side BD from the centre A . Therefore (Theorem 7)

$$(LMPQ) = (BDPK). \tag{1}$$

On the other hand, the points L, M, P, Q are respectively the projections of points D, B, P and K from the centre C ; therefore

$$(LMPQ) = (DBPK). \tag{2}$$

But, as a result of Theorem 8, we have

$$(DBPK) = \frac{1}{(BDPK)} \cdot$$

Therefore, multiplying equations (1) and (2) term by term, we obtain

$$(LMPQ)^2 = 1. \tag{3}$$

In so far as the equation $(LMPQ) = 1$ is impossible in this case (see Section 5), then we have from (3)

$$(LMPQ) = -1. \tag{4}$$

Through the point K there pass four straight lines, which intersect the diagonal LM at the points L, M, P and Q (the two sides and two diagonals of the complete quadrangle $ABCD$), from the equation (4) on the basis of Theorem 6 we deduce, that these straight lines form a harmonic pencil:

$$(KL, KM, BD, AC) = -1.$$

Thus, the theorem is proved.

T h e o r e m 13. <u>The pair of points on the diagonal of a complete quadrangle, through each of which passes one of the sides of the quadrangle, divides harmonically the pair of points on the same diagonal, through each of which pass two of the sides of the quadrangle</u>.

Thus, for the diagonal LM of the complete quadrange $ABCD$ (Fig. 16) the points of the first pair are P and Q , and the points of the second pair are L and M . The truth of this theorem follows from the equation (4).

8. CONIC SECTIONS

Let the straight lines l and m intersecting at the point S, form an angle other than a right one. The straight line m, revolving round the stationary straight line l, will describe a continuous surface, the circular cone K, consisting of two sheets joined by the point S - the <u>vertex</u> of the cone.

Intersecting the cone K by means of some plane α we obtain a curve q called a <u>conic section</u>. Assuming that α does not pass through the vertex S of the cone K, we shall distinguish the following cases:

(1) The plane α intersects all the generators of one sheet of the cone; then q is a closed oval curve, called an <u>ellipse</u> (Fig. 17). A particular case of the ellipse, when α is perpendicular to l, is a circle.

(2) The **plane** α is parallel to a generator of the cone; then q is an infinite open curve called a <u>parabola</u> (Fig. 18).

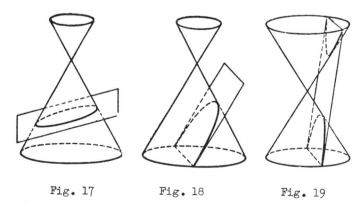

Fig. 17   Fig. 18   Fig. 19

(3) The plane α intersects both sheets of the cone. Then q is an open curve consisting of two infinite branches; it

is called a hyperbola (Fig. 19).

We note that a point and also a pair of intersecting straight lines can be regarded as sections of the cone by a plane passing through its vertex S ; if S is a point at infinity, that is if the cone degenerates into a circular cylinder, these straight lines would be parallel. Let us, however, agree in the future to apply the term "conic sections" only to curves - the ellipse, the parabola and the hyperbola.

Let the circle x be the section of cone K by the plane β perpendicular to the axis l of the cone (and not passing through S , of course). If the circle x is projected from the vertex S of the cone K onto a plane α , then its projection will be a conic section q . Hence it follows that all projective properties of a circle are transferred to each conic section.

We shall make use of this note when proving theorems establishing the projective properties of conic sections. We shall demonstrate proofs for the case of a circle and the truth of the corresponding theorems for any conic section will follow automatically.

9. POLAR PROPERTIES OF CONIC SECTIONS

Through the point P lying in the plane of a conic section q, but not on it, draw a line l intersecting q in the points M and N. Denote the fourth harmonic point of M, N; P by Q. If the straight line l is made to rotate about the point P in the plane of the given conic section, Q will trace out a curve π called the <u>polar</u> of the point P with respect to q. The point P is called the <u>pole</u> of the curve π.

We shall call the tangent at a point lying on a conic section q the polar of that point.

In a similar manner we define the polar of a point with respect to a figure consisting of two intersecting or parallel straight lines. If the point lies on one of the given straight lines, then this line is its polar. The polar of the point of intersection of two straight lines with respect to these lines is indefinite.

From the definition of a polar it follows that the polar of the centre of a circle with respect to that circle is a straight line at infinity.

T h e o r e m   14. <u>The polar of a point with respect to a circle is a straight line perpendicular to the join of the given point and the centre of the circle.</u> (Here we regard the given point as distinct from the centre of the circle).

If the given point P lies on the given circle $\varkappa$ then the theorem is self-evident. Therefore we further discuss the case when P does not lies on $\varkappa$.

Let us construct a straight line PK, where K is the centre of the circle $\varkappa$. Let it intersect the circle $\varkappa$ at the points A and B. Let Q be the point inverse to P with respect to $\varkappa$. Let the straight line l passing through P and intersecting the circle $\varkappa$ at the points M and N be other than the straight line PK.

We construct a circle μ using the segment MN as a diameter.

27

Then, we draw a circle ν through P and Q , with its centre
on the straight line l. . The circle is orthogonal to the
circle ϰ , since it passes through two different points inverse with respect to ϰ (Theorem 1). It is also orthogonal
to the circle μ , since its centre lies on the radical axis
of the circles ϰ and μ (Theorem 4). Its points of intersection with the diameter MN of the circle μ and its continu-
ation are therefore inverse with respect to μ (Theorem 2).

The angle PQR , subtended by a semicircle of the circle ν ,
is a right angle, therefore the point R lies on the perpendicular to PK at Q .

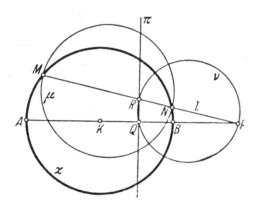

Fig. 20

By applying Theorem 11 to the circles ϰ and μ we ascertain
that points Q and R belong to the polar π of the point P with
respect to the circle ϰ . Therefore, π is the perpendicular
to the straight line PK at the point Q , which was the required result. The above considerations apply whether P lies
outside or inside the circle ϰ . For clarity we illustrate
each of these cases by means of a separate drawing (Figs. 20
and 21).

If we keep to the letter of the definition then we should
regard as the polar of point P the chord of circle ϰ , passing
through Q and perpendicular to PK , the ends of the chord
being the points at which tangents from P touch the circle ϰ
(Compare Fig. 4). Certain considerations, however, discussed
below, lead us to call the whole straight line containing the

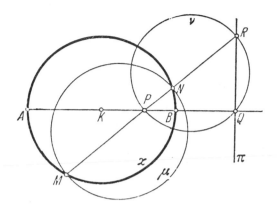

Fig. 21

above chord the polar of point P .

A direct corollary of Theorem 14 is:

T h e o r e m   15. <u>The polar of a point with respect to</u>
<u>a conic section is a straight line</u>.

From the preceding results it is easy to draw the following
conclusions:

If the point P lies outside a conic section q , that is,
if it is possible to draw a straight line through P such
that it has no common points with q , then its polar intersects q at the points of contact of tangents from P to q .

If the point P lies inside the conic section q then its
polar has no common point with q .

If tangents are drawn at points A and B of a conic section
q , they will intersect at the pole of the straight line AB .

T h e o r e m   16. <u>If the point Q lies on the polar of</u>
<u>the point P with respect to a given conic section, then P lies</u>
<u>on the polar of the point Q</u>.

It is sufficient to ascertain that the theorem is true in
the case when the given conic section is a circle; let us
denote it by x and its centre by K (Fig. 22). The point S

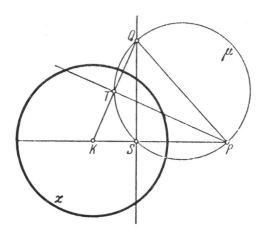

Fig. 22

inverse to P with respect to the circle $\varkappa$ lies on the polar of point P (Theorem 11) and the angle PSQ is a right angle. The circle μ , constructed on the segment PQ as diameter, passes through the point S and therefore is orthogonal to the circle $\varkappa$. Let the straight line KQ intersect the circle μ at the point T.

The point T is inverse to Q with respect to $\varkappa$ (Theorem 2) and the angle PTQ is a right one. Hence and from the definition of a polar and from Theorem 14 we conclude that the straight line PT is the polar of the point Q with respect to $\varkappa$. The theorem is thus proved.

The theorem is true also when the point P lies on the circle $\varkappa$, since the polar of every point on the tangent to $\varkappa$ at the point P passes through P.

We note that the points P and Q in Fig. 22 lie outside the circle $\varkappa$. From the proof of Theorem 16 it follows that it is useful to regard their polars not as chords of $\varkappa$ but as infinitely extended straight lines, otherwise it would be necessary to introduce a number of reservations into the statement of Theorem 16.

Let the straight line l intersect the circle of radius r ,
centre   at the points A and B . Let $AC = CB = d$, $OC = h$,
where C is the midpoint of chord AB . Obviously, $d^2 = r^2 - h^2$.
Hence we obtain imaginary values for the quantity d , if
$h > r$. We shall agree to a convention that in this case,
too, the straight line l intersects the given circle, but
the points of their intersection, A and B , are imaginary.
The introduction of the idea of imaginary points turns out
to be very fruitful; in particular, it explains why the
external parts of the chord which joins the points of
contact of tangents from a point to a circle should be
regarded as part of the polar of the point with respect
to the circle.

T h e o r e m   17. <u>The polar of a point with respect to</u>
<u>two straight lines is a straight line which passes through</u>
<u>the point of intersection of the given straight lines</u>
<u>(parallel to them if they are parallel)</u>.

Let the straight lines m and n intersect at the point O
(Fig. 23). Through P let us draw a straight line l intersecting m and n in different points M and N , and let us
denote by Q the fourth harmonic point of $M, N; P$. The straight

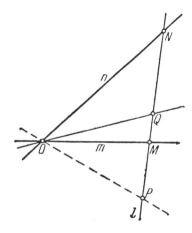

Fig. 23

lines m, n; OP, OQ form a harmonic pencil (Theorem 6).

Therefore their points of intersection with any straight
line other than OP, passing through P, will form a harmonic
range. It follows from here that the straight line OQ is the
polar of the point P. If O is a point at infinity, then
the straight lines m, n and OQ are parallel.

10. THE THEOREMS OF BRIANCHON AND PASCAL

We shall make the following preliminary observation. If tangents are drawn to a circle x at points A and B on it, and then equal segments are marked off on them in the same direction from the line AB, so that $AA_1 = BB_1$, then a circle can be drawn through the points A_1 and B_1 such that AA_1 and BB_1 are its tangents (Fig. 24). This follows from the symmetry of the given figure with respect to that diameter of circle x , which is perpendicular to the chord AB.

T h e o r e m 18. (Brianchon). <u>In a hexagon circumscribed about a conic section, the diagonals joining opposite vertices are concurrent</u>.

Obviously, it is sufficient to prove this theorem for the case of a circle.

Let the sides *AB, BC, CD, DE, EF* and *FA* of the hexagon

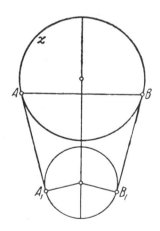

Fig. 24

33

ABCDEF touch the circle ϰ at the points *a, b, c, d, e, f* respectively (Fig. 25). Let us take an arbitrary segment *MN* and let us construct on the rays *aB, bB, cD, dD, eF, fF* respectively the segments

$$a\alpha = b\beta = c\gamma = d\delta = e\varepsilon = f\zeta = MN. \qquad (1)$$

Let us draw through the points α and δ , the circle λ , which touches the straight lines *Aα* and *Eδ* ; through the points γ and ζ the circle μ which touches the straight lines *Cγ* and *Aζ* and through the points ε and β the circle ν touching the straight lines *Eε* and *Cβ* . The permissibility of these constructions follows from equations (1).

It is easy to ascertain that the straight lines *AD, BE* and *CF* are the radical axes of the following pairs of circles respectively: λ and μ , λ and ν , μ and ν . For example, the points *B* and *E* lie on the radical axis of circles λ and ν , since *Bα* = *Bβ* and *Eδ* = *Eε* (*Bα* = *MN* — *aB*,   *Bβ* = *MN* — *bB*; *Eδ* = *MN* + *Ed*, *Eε* = *MN* + *Ee*) .

Therefore (Theorem 5) the straight lines *AD, BE* and *CF* all intersect at one point - the radical centre of the circles λ, μ, ν . The theorem is thus proved.

Brianchon's theorem holds also in the case when two adjacent sides of a hexagon lie in one straight line. Their common vertex, in that case, will be the point at which this straight line touches the circle.

Let us examine, for instance, a quadrilateral *ACDF* circumscribed about a circle and regard it as a hexagon *ABCDEF* , where *B* and *E* are the points at which *AC* and *DF* touch the circle ϰ (Fig. 26). According to Brianchon's theorem the straight line *BE* passes through the point of intersection *S* of the diagonals *AD* and *CF* of the given quadrilateral. In the same way, we ascertain that the straight line *MN*, joining the points at which *AF* and *CD* touch the circle ϰ , also passes through *S* . Thus, in a quadrilateral, circumscribed about a circle, the straight lines joining the points, at which opposite sides touch the circle, and the diagonals of the quadrilateral are concurrent.

T h e o r e m   19. (Pascal). <u>The points of intersection</u>

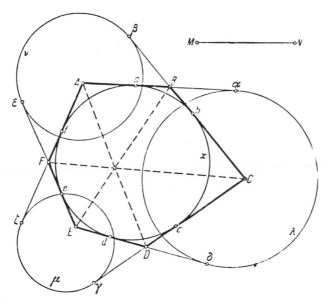

Fig. 25

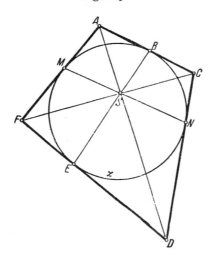

Fig. 26

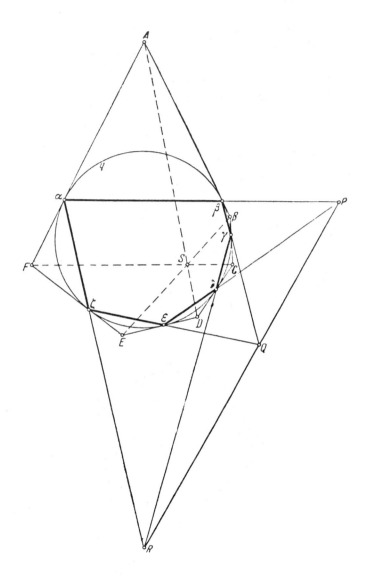

Fig. 27

of the opposite sides of a hexagon inscribed in a conic sec-
are collinear*.

Let the sides αβ and δε of a hexagon αβγδεζ inscribed into
a conic section q intersect at a point P ; let the sides
and εζ intersect at a point Q and the sides γδ and ζα at
point R (Fig. 27). Let us construct tangents to q at the
vertices of this hexagon and let us denote the hexagon thus
formed by ABCDEF .

The point P lies on the polar αβ of the point A and also
on the polar δε of the point D ; therefore (Theorem 16) the
straight line AD is the polar of point P . Similarly, we
make sure that the straight lines BE and CF are polars of
the points Q and R respectively.

According to Brianchon's theorem, the straight lines AD ,
BE and CF are concurrent at the point S . Since the polars
of points P, Q and R pass through S , therefore P,Q and R
lie on the polar of S , i.e. on the same straight line, which
is the required result.

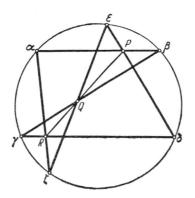

Fig. 28

*This is one of the basic theorems of projective geometry.
It was formulated and proved for the first time by the sixteen
year old Blaise Pascal (1623-1662) who at an early age revealed
brilliant mathematical gifts. The theorem of Brianchon joined
the body of knowledge much later, approximately 150 years after
Pascal's discovery.

Pascal's theorem holds also when two neighbouring vertices
of the hexagon inscribed in a conic section coincide. In
this case we must consider the side of the hexagon defined
by these vertices to be the tangent to the conic section at
that point, where both the vertices are situated.

The theorems of Pascal and Brianchon also hold, as is seen
from their proofs, when the hexagons are starlike.

Part Two

GEOMETRICAL CONSTRUCTIONS
WITH THE AID OF A RULER

11. THE CONSTRUCTION OF CERTAIN RECTILINEAR FIGURES BY MEANS OF A RULER

<u>Problem 1.</u> <u>On a straight line *l*, three separate points, A. B and C are given. Construct a point D such that together with C it divides harmonically the pair of points A, B</u> .

The concept of the construction based on the harmonic properties of a complete quadrangle is obvious. All the same, because of the importance of the problem, we shall consider in detail all stages of construction.

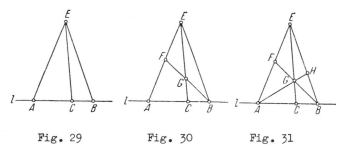

Fig. 29   Fig. 30   Fig. 31

We take any point *E* outside the straight line *l* and we draw straight lines *AE, BE, CE* (Fig. 29). On *AE* we take a point *F* , other than *A* and *E* and we construct the straight line *BF* intersecting *CE* at the point *G* (Fig. 30). We draw the straight line *AG* intersecting *BE* at the point *H* (Fig. 31). The straight line *FH* intersects *l* at the required point *D* (Fig. 32).

Indeed, the straight line *AB* is a diagonal of a complete quadrangle *EFGH*; therefore, according to Theorem 13, $(ABCD) = -1$.

In Fig. 33 the same construction is carried out for the case when the point *C* lies outside the segment *AB*.

<u>Problem 2.</u> <u>Three different straight lines *a, b, c* belonging</u>

41

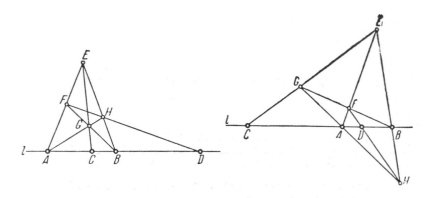

Fig. 32   Fig. 33

to a pencil of lines are given. Construct a straight line
_d_ , which, together with _c_ , will divide the pair _a_, _b_ harmonically.

We construct a straight line _l_ , not passing through the
centre of the pencil, i.e. through the point of intersection
of the given straight lines. Let _l_ intersect the lines in
A, B, C respectively. We construct the harmonic conjugate of
C with respect to A and B (Problem 1) and we draw a straight
line joining it and the centre of the pencil.

Problem 3. To draw a straight line through a given point
A and the inaccessible point* of intersection of the given
straight lines _a_ and _b_ .

The construction is shown in Fig. 34. Its correctness is
proved by means of the following considerations. Let us denote the inaccessible point of intersection of straight lines
_a_ and _b_ by X. The straight lines _a_ and _b_ are two sides and the
straight lines XA and XF are diagonals of a complete quadrangle BDCE , therefore XA is the fourth harmonic straight
line of _a_, _b_; XF (Theorem 12). In exactly the same way, considering the complete quadrangle BDGH, we make sure that
XK is the fourth harmonic straight line to the same straight

---

*The parts of a figure which lie outside the boundaries of
the drawing are called its inaccessible parts.

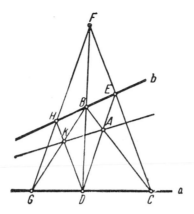

Fig. 34

lines $a, b; XF$. Thus, the straight lines XA and XK coincide, and so AK is the straight line required.

We propose that the reader himself investigates the case when the point A lies outside the strip enclosed by the straight lines a and b .

Problem 4. Given a conic section q and a point P not on q. Construct the polar π of point P.

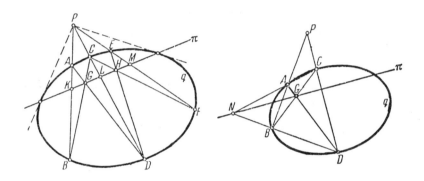

Fig. 35   Fig. 36

In Figs. 35, 36 and 37 different variations of the construction are given, based on the harmonic properties of a complete quadrangle.

We shall examine the configuration of Fig. 35. We construct points K, L, M on the secants PA, PC, PE in such a way that the conditions

$$(ABPK) = (CDPL) = (EFPM) = -1 \qquad (1)$$

are fulfilled. From the properties of the complete quadrangles $ABCD$·and $CDFE$, the straight lines KL and LM are the respective diagonals of these quadrangles, the first one passing through the point G and the second one passing

44

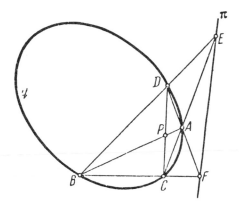

Fig. 37

through the point H . But from the equations (1) it follows
that points K, L, M belong to the polar π of point P , and
so π passes through G and H.   In fact, the points K, L, M
are not constructed; we considered them only in order to
give a foundation to the proposed solution.

The above construction can be simplified by omitting to
draw the secant PE , as the diagonal KL of the complete quadrangle $ABCD$ must pass through the point G and through the
point of intersection of the sides AC and BD (Fig. 36).

The construction carried out in Fig. 37 is based on the
following: from the previous construction we have that
the straight lines PE and PF (not drawn in the figure) are
the respective polars of the points F and E . Hence and
from theorem 16 the polar π of the point P passes through E
and F .

Problem 5. Given a conic section q and the point P not on
q . Draw tangents to q from P .

We construct the polar π of the point P and we join P by
means of straight lines to the points of intersection of π
and q . In Fig. 35, the tangents from P are drawn as dotted
lines.

If *q* and π do not intersect, then the required tangents do not exist.

Problem 6. Given a conic section and a straight line π. Construct the pole *P* of this straight line.

We take any two points *A* and *B* on π . We construct the polar *a* of point *A* and the polar *b* of point *B* . The straight lines *a* and *b* will intersect in the required point *P* (Theorem 16).

Problem 7. Draw a tangent through the point *P* on the given conic section.

We draw an arbitrary secant through *P* and we find its pole *Q* . The straight line *PQ* is the required tangent.

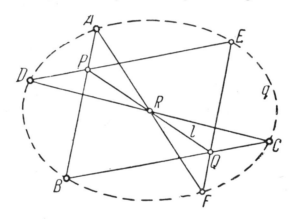

Fig. 38

Problem 8. Given five points *A, B, C, D, E* of a conic section *q* . Construct a sixth point of the curve *q*_.

We regard the points *A, B, C, D, E* as five consecutive vertices of Pascal's hexagon inscribed into the curve *q* (Fig. 38). We construct the straight lines *AB* and *DE* and draw an arbitrary line *l* through their point of intersection *P* . Let the straight lines *BC* and *CD* intersect *l* at points *Q* and *R* respectively. We draw the straight lines *EQ* and *AR* , their common point *F* lies on the conic section *q* .

Indeed, the points of intersection of the opposite sides
(AB and DE, BC and EF, CD and FA) of the hexagon $ABCDEF$ are
collinear; if the straight line AR intersected q once again
at the point F' other than F, the straight line EF' would not
pass through the point Q, which would contradict Pascal's
theorem.

N o t e. If one point of intersection of some straight
line with a conic section, which is defined by five points,
is known, then, by applying the above method, it is possible
to construct the second point of intersection, using a ruler.
It is impossible, however, to construct by means of a ruler
alone the points of intersection of a given straight line with
a conic section, given by five points, if neither of the
points of intersection is given.

Problem 9. Given five points A, B, C, D, E of a conic section
q. Construct a tangent to q at one of these points.

We shall construct a tangent to q at the point D (Fig. 39).
Regarding the straight lines AB, BC, CD, the tangent to q at
D, DE and EA as the sides of an inscribed hexagon, we find
the point of intersection P of the straight lines BC and DE,
and the point of intersection Q of the straight lines CD and
EA. Let us denote the common point of the straight lines

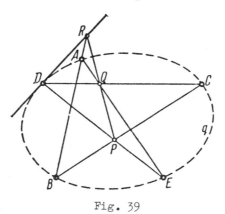

Fig. 39

AB and PQ by R. The straight line DR is the required tangent.

Problem 10. Given four points A, B, C and D of a conic

section _q_ and a tangent _a_ to _q_ at point _A_ . Construct a fifth
point of the curve _q_ .

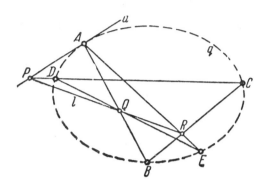

Fig. 40

Regarding the straight lines a, AB, BC, CD, DE, EA as the sides
of a hexagon inscribed in q, we find the point of intersection
P of the straight lines a and CD. We draw any straight
line l through P . Let it intersect AB at the point Q and
BC at the point R (Fig. 40). The common point E of the
straight lines AR and DQ lies on the curve q .

Problem 11. Given five tangents a, b, c, d and e to the conic
section _q_ . Construct a sixth tangent to _q_ .

We regard a, b, c, d and e as five of the sides of a hexagon,
circumscribed about q (Fig. 41).

Let the straight lines a and b intersect at the point A ,
the straight lines d and e intersect at the point D . We
draw the straight line AD , we take an arbitrary point K on
it, other than A or D , and we construct the straight lines
BK and CK . Let CK intersect e at the point E . The straight
line EF is the required tangent.

Indeed, if we draw a tangent f to q from the point F , we
form a hexagon $abcdef$ circumscribed about q . The straight
lines joining the opposite vertices of this hexagon are concurrent, according to Brianchon's theorem. Two of these
straight lines, AD and CF intersect at the point K . There-

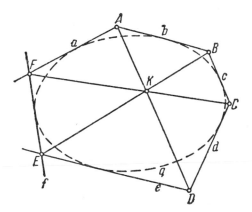

Fig. 41

fore the tangent f should pass through the point E , which
lies both on e and on BK .

Problem 12. Given five tangents a, b, c, d, e to the conic
section q . Construct the point at which the straight line
a touches the curve q .

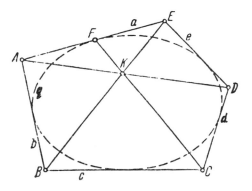

Fig. 42

We have noted before (see Section 10) that Brianchon's
theorem holds even when two adjacent sides of the circumscribed hexagon coincide. In this case the point at which
that straight line touches the given conic section is taken

as the vertex, common to these two sides.

We carry out the construction as follows (Fig. 42). Regarding the straight lines a, a (twice!) b, c, d, e as the sides of a hexagon circumscribed about q, we obtain five vertices of the hexagon A, B, C, D, E. We draw the straight lines AD and BE. Let them intersect at the point K. We construct the straight line CK and we find the point of intersection F of this line with the straight line a. The point F is the sixth vertex of the hexagon and it follows that the straight line a touches the conic section q at that point.

Applying Pascal's and Brianchon's theorems, the reader can easily solve the seven problems below, using a ruler alone.

(1) Given four points A, B, C, D of a conic section q and a tangent a to it at the point A. Construct a tangent to q at the point B.

(2) Given three points, A, B and C of a conic section q, a tangent a to q at the point A and a tangent b to q at the point B. Construct a fourth point on the curve q.

(3) Given three points A, B and C of a conic section q, a tangent a to q at the point A and a tangent b to q at the point B. Construct a tangent to q at the point C.

(4) Given four tangents a, b, c and d to the conic section q and the point A at which the straight line a touches q. Construct a fifth tangent to q.

(5) Given four tangents a, b, c and d to the conic section q and the point A at which the straight line a touches q. Construct the point at which the line b touches q.

(6) Given three tangents a, b, c to the conic section q, the point A at which the straight line a touches q, and the point B at which the straight line b touches q. Construct a fourth tangent to q.

(7) Given three tangents, a, b, c to the conic section q, the point A at which the straight line a touches q and the point B at which the straight line b touches q. Construct the point at which the line c touches q.

13. RULER CONSTRUCTIONS, GIVEN TWO PARALLEL STRAIGHT LINES

In the constructions discussed below we shall make frequent use of the following theorem:

T h e o r e m 20. <u>The straight line that passes through the point of intersection of the diagonals of a trapezium and through the point of intersection of its non-parallel sides, bisects each of the parallel sides of the trapezium.</u>

This theorem can be proved on the basis of the harmonic properties of the complete quadrangle $CDEF$ (Fig. 43); since the fourth harmonic point of the points A, B; K is a point at infinity, then $AK = KB$.

Another proof is also possible, based on quite elementary considerations. We have the following pairs of similar triangles: AKE and DLE, KBE and LCE, AKF and CLF, KBF and DLF. Hence we conclude that

$$\frac{AK}{DL} = \frac{KE}{LE}, \quad \frac{KB}{LC} = \frac{KE}{LE}$$

and

$$\frac{AK}{LC} = \frac{KF}{FL}, \quad \frac{KB}{DL} = \frac{KF}{FL}$$

From these relationships the following proportions follow:

$$\frac{AK}{KB} = \frac{DL}{LC}, \quad \frac{AK}{KB} = \frac{LC}{DL}.$$

Multiplying together the latter two equations we get

$$\left(\frac{AK}{KB}\right)^2 = 1.$$

Therefore $AK = KB$.

<u>Problem 13.</u> <u>Given a segment AB and its midpoint K .</u>

<u>Through a given point D draw a straight line parallel to the
straight line AB;</u>

We construct the straight lines AD, BD, BE and KE where E
is any point on the ray AD (see Fig. 43). Let us denote the

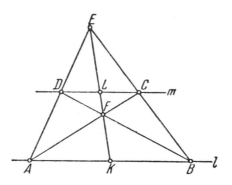

Fig. 43

point of intersection of the straight lines BD and KE by F .
We draw the straight line AF . It intersects BE at a certain
point C . We construct the straight line CD ; it is parallel
to the straight line AB .

<u>Problem 14. The straight lines l and m are parallel. Bi-</u>
<u>sect the segment AB on l .</u>

We take an arbitrary point E , lying neither on l nor on
m (see Fig. 43) and we draw the straight lines AE and BE .
Let these straight lines intersect m at the respective points
D and C . We construct the straight lines AC and BD. We
denote their point of intersection by F . The straight line
EF passes through the mid-point of the segment AB .

<u>Problem 15. Through the point A lying outside the given</u>
<u>straight lines l and m , draw a straight line parallel to</u>
<u>the given ones.</u>

We bisect an arbitrary segment on the straight line l
(Problem 14) and through A we draw a line parallel to l
(Problem 13).

<u>Problem 16. Given two parallel lines l and m and a seg-</u>
<u>ment AB on l , construct a segment n times as long as AB .</u>

(*n* is a whole number).

Through an arbitrary point *K* (Fig. 44) outside the straight lines *l* and *m* we draw a straight line *p* parallel to the given ones (Problem 15). We construct the straight lines *AK* and *BK*. Let them intersect *m* at points *A'* and *B'* respectively. We construct the straight line *BA'* intersecting *p* at the point *L* and the straight line *LB'* intersecting *l* at the point *C*.

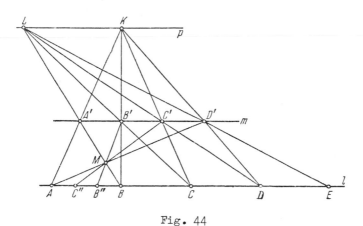

Fig. 44

Then *AB* = *BC*. Continuing the construction we obtain the segments *CD*, *DE* and so on; each equals the segment *AB*.

Problem 17. Given two parallel straight lines *l* and *m*, and a segment *AB* and a point *C* on *l*. Construct a segment *CD* equal to the segment *AB* on *l*.

We draw a line parallel to the given lines through an arbitrary point *K* outside of *l* and *m*. Further construction is obvious from Fig. 45. The problem has two solutions (segments *CD* and *CD'*).

Problem 18. Given two parallel straight lines *l* and *m* and a segment *AB* on *l*. Divide this segment into *n* equal parts.

Let the number of equal parts into which the segment is to be divided be three. If we increase the segment *AB* three times in the same way as it was done in Problem 16, we shall

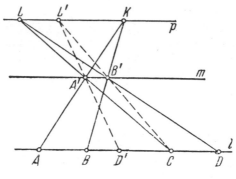

Fig. 45

obtain on the straight line m (Fig.44) equal segments
$A'B'$, $B'C'$, $C'D'$. We then draw the straight lines AD', BA' ;
we denote their point of intersection by M. Finally, we construct the straight lines $B'M$ and $C'M$. They divide the
segment AB into three equal parts at B'' and C'' .

Problem 19. Given two parallel straight lines l and m and
a segment AB on l. Construct $\frac{1}{n}$ th part of the segment AB
(n is a whole number).

According to the condition in the problem, it is sufficient
to construct only one segment equal to $\frac{1}{n} AB$, while in the
previous problem it was necessary to construct n such segments.

We shall demonstrate an elegant solution of this problem
put forward by Brianchon.

Through an arbitrary point K outside of the straight lines
l and m we draw straight lines AK and BK (Fig. 46). Let them
intersect m at the points α and β . We construct the straight
lines $A\beta$, $B\alpha$ (intersecting at the point γ), $K\gamma$ (intersects
l at the point C), αC (intersects $A\beta$ at the point δ), $K\delta$
(intersects l at the point D). We shall prove that $AD = \frac{1}{3} AB$.
On investigating the complete quadrangle $\alpha\delta\gamma K$, we came
to the conclusion that the points A, C; D, B form a harmonic
range, therefore

$$AD : DC = AB : CB.$$

But $AB = 2\,CB$(see Problem 14) therefore from the preceding equation we get: $AD = 2DC$; therefore $AD = \frac{1}{3}\,AB$.

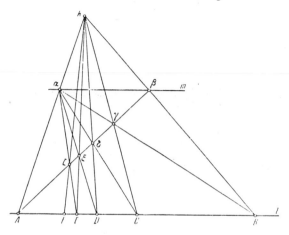

Fig. 46

If we draw the additional straight lines αD (intersects $A\beta$ at the point ξ) and $K\xi$ (intersects l at the point E), we obtain the segment $AE = \frac{1}{4}\,AB$.

Having further constructed the straight lines αE (intersects $A\beta$ at the point ζ) and $K\zeta$ (intersects l in F) we obtain the segment $AF = \frac{1}{5}\,AB$.

In order to prove the two latter equations it is sufficient to take into account that both the points $A,-D$; E, B and the points A, E; F, B form harmonic ranges.

Continuing this construction, we shall find one sixth, one seventh, ... part of the segment AB.

14. RULER CONSTRUCTIONS, GIVEN A PARALLELOGRAM
OR A SQUARE

Making use of a parallelogram, it is possible to solve the
following problem.

Problem 20. Through a given point draw a straight line
parallel to a given straight line *l* .

Through the point of intersection of the diagonals of the
parallelogram we draw a straight line parallel to one of its
sides. Then two equal segments *EF* and *FG* form on the given
straight line (Fig. 47). Thus, we come to Problem 13. Cases

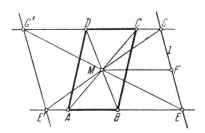

Fig. 47

when *l* is parallel to *BC* and *l* is parallel to *AB* lead to
Problem 15. The second method of solution consists of the
construction of points *G′* (the intersection of straight lines
CD and *EM*) and *E′* (the intersection of straight lines *AB* and
GM). The straight line *E′G′* is parallel to the straight
line *l* ; therefore we have again arrived at Problem 15.

Using a square, it is possible, in addition to problems
14-20, to solve the following two problems.

Problem 21. Draw a perpendicular through a given point

56

K to a given straight line *l* .

Let the square *ABCD* be given (Fig. 48). We construct its diagonals and through their point of intersection *M* we draw a straight line *EF* parallel to *l* (Problem 20). We then construct *FG* parallel to *AB* and *GH* parallel to *AC* .

It is easy to prove that *HM* is perpendicular to *EF*. Indeed it follows from the construction that $CF = GD = DH$; further, $MD = MC$, $\angle MDH = \angle MCF = 45°$. Thus the triangles *MDH* and *MCF* are congruent. Hence we deduce that

$$\angle HMF = \angle HMC + \angle CMF = \angle HMC + \angle HMD = \angle DMC = 90°.$$

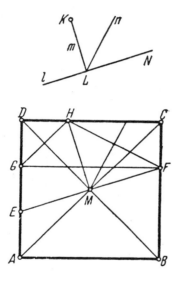

Fig. 48

This means that in order to solve the problem it is necessary to draw a straight line *m* parallel to *HM* through the point *K* . This straight line is the required perpendicular.

Problem 22 . To bisect a given right angle.

Let it be required to bisect the given right angle *KLN* (Fig. 48). In so far as the sides of this angle are parallel to the the sides of the angle *FMH* (see the preceding problem), it is

sufficient therefore, in order to solve this problem, to draw
a straight line through l , parallel to the bisector of the
angle FMH, which is, as is easily seen, perpendicular to
the straight line FH . Indeed, the triangle FMH is isosceles,
since $MF = MH$ as a result of the congruency of triangles MDH
and MCF .

Therefore the straight line n passing through the point L
perpendicular to the straight line FH (Problem 21) will be
the required bisector of the angle KLN .

15. RULER CONSTRUCTIONS, GIVEN A CIRCLE AND ITS CENTRE

If a problem on construction is soluble by means of a ruler and compasses, then, as is well known, its solution by algebraic methods can be reduced to the construction of the roots of one or several linear and quadratic equations. In this connexion it is customary to call such problems 'problems of the second degree'.

The following fact deserves attention; every construction problem of the second degree can be solved by means of a ruler alone, if in the plane of the construction a circle has been drawn and its centre indicated*.

In order to prove that, it is sufficient to make sure that by means of this set-up it is possible to find the points of intersection of a circle, given by a centre and a radius, with a straight line, and also the points of intersection of two circles, given in the same manner. Indeed, in construction problems the compasses are used only for carrying out these two operations**.

---

*This fact was established by the French mathematician Poncelet, and, independently, by the German mathematician Steiner. Jean-Victor Poncelet (1789-1867) had been an officer in Napoleon's army in his youth. He participated in the invasion of Russia in 1812, was taken prisoner and lived in Saratov for two years, where he occupied himself by investigations into projective geometry.
    Jakob Steiner (1796-1867) was the son of a Swiss peasant. At the age of 19, practically unable to write, he enrolled at the school of the famous pedagogue Pestalozzi. In his 39th year he was elected a full member of the Berlin Academy of Sciences.
**It is not possible to describe a circle by means of a ruler, but it is possible to construct any number of points on the circle, if five of the points on it are known (Problem 8) see also Problem 29 below.

The corresponding constructions will be considered in Problems 30 and 31. In a number of cases, however, we can manage without applying them (the operations) making use, instead, of simpler steps in order to solve the problems. We shall therefore first consider several basic constructive problems and we shall show ways of solving them, which are convenient in practice.

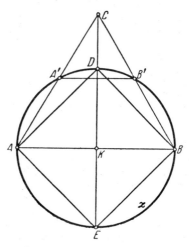

Fig. 49

We shall take it that in the plane of each problem of this section there has been drawn an auxiliary circle x and its centre K has been constructed.

Problem 23. To construct a square

We construct the diameter AB of the circle x (Fig. 49) and we draw its chord A'B', parallel to AB (Problem 13). Through the point of intersection C of the straight lines AA' and BB' we draw the straight line CK. It intersects the circle at the points D and E. The quadrangle ADBE is a square.

Hence we conclude, that all problems of Sections 13 and 14 can be solved by means of the ruler, if a circle has been drawn and its centre constructed.

Problem 24. Through a given point draw a straight line parallel to a given straight line l.

If l passes through K , we have Problem 13. Otherwise it is necessary to construct any straight line parallel to l , as a result of which we arrive at Problem 15. The construction is obvious from Fig. 50; the straight line GH is parallel to l .

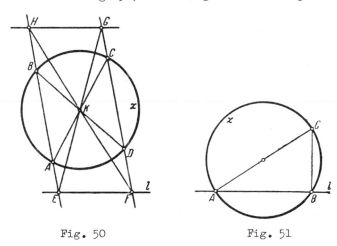

Fig. 50   Fig. 51

Problem 25. Through a given point draw a straight line perpendicular to the given straight line l .

If l intersects the circle $\varkappa$ at the points A and B , but does not pass through the centre, we draw the diameter AC of the circle $\varkappa$. The straight line CB is perpendicular to l (Fig. 51). Then we draw a line parallel to CB through the given point. In other cases we apply the same method, but first we construct a straight line parallel to l and intersecting the circle $\varkappa$ at two points not on the same diameter.

Problem 26. Through the given point P draw a straight line, at a given angle $MON = \alpha$ to the given straight line l .

The solution is given in Fig. 52, where KA is parallel to OM, KB to ON, KC to l, AD to BC, BE to AC, PD' to KD, PE' to KE .

If α is acute or obtuse, the problem has two solutions.

Problem 27. To double the given angle $MON = \alpha$.
Parallel to the straight line OM we draw the diameter AB

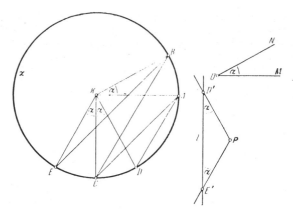

Fig. 52

of the circle $\varkappa$ and parallel to the straight line ON we draw the chord AC (Fig. 53). Then $\angle BKC = 2\alpha$. The side OR of the required angle MOR is parallel to the straight line KC .

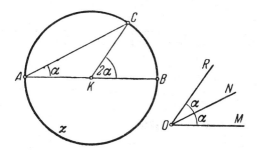

Fig. 53

Problem 28. Construct the bisector of the given angle $MON = \alpha$.

The construction is carried out in Fig. 54, where AB is parallel to OM, KC to ON, OR to AC .

Problem 29. Given a segment AB and a ray h with a vertex C . Construct a segment CD equal to AB on h .

We construct a parallelogram $KABH$ and we draw a ray KF parallel to h (Fig. 55). Let the rays KH and KF intersect the circle $\varkappa$ at points E and F. We draw the straight lines EF and HL parallel to EF until it intersects with KF at the point L. We construct the parallelogram $CKLD$. The segment CD is the required one.

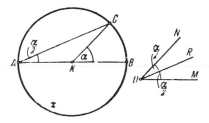

Fig. 54

The construction becomes simpler if the points K, A, B or the point K and the ray h lie in one straight line.

This construction enables us to find points of a circle on straight lines passing through its centre, if its centre and radius are given.

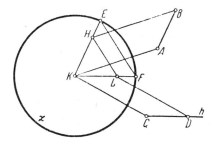

Fig. 55

Problem 30. Construct the points of intersection of the given straight line l with the circle $\varkappa$ given by its centre M and radius MN, but not sketched in.

Parallel to the straight line MN we draw the radius KL of the circle x (Fig. 56). We construct straight lines KM and LN and we find their point of intersection A - the centre of similitude of the circle x and µ (it is the external centre of similitude that is constructed in the figure).

Further, we find the straight line l' , which is the line resulting from l , when a transformation of similitude*, centre A , is carried out on the given figure, changing circle µ into x .

In order to do that we take any point B on l , we construct segments BA and BM , we draw the straight line KC parallel to MB through K until it intersects AB at the point C , and we draw l' parallel to l through C . Let l' intersect the circle x at the points D and E . The straight lines AD and AE intersect the straight line l at the required points F and G .

If points D and E coincide then l touches the circle µ . If l' has no common points with the circle x , then l has no common points with the circle µ .

If the point A is at infinity, then the internal centre of similitude of x and µ ought to be taken, instead of the external one.

How will the construction alter in the case when the circles x and µ are concentric?

Problem 31. Given the centres M and N of circles µ and ν and their radii. Construct the points of intersection of these circles.

We shall begin by constructing the radical axis of the given circles. Suppose that A is any point on the circle ν and B any point on the circle ν and that at least one of the points A, B does not lie on the straight line MN (Fig. 57).

We construct the segment AB , we find its mid-point C and we draw the straight lines MN, MC, NC, AD perpendicular to

---

*i.e. constructing a similar figure to the given one by projecting it, centre A , a bit further on the plane.

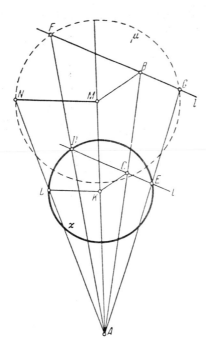

Fig. 56

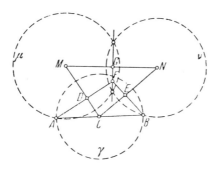

Fig. 57

CM, BE perpendicular to *CN* . Let the straight lines *AD* and
BE intersect at the point *F* ; we construct *FG* perpendicular
to *MN*. The straight line *FG* is the radical axis of the circles μ and ν . Indeed, having constructed a circle γ , using
the segment *AB* as a diameter, we note that the point *F* is the
radical centre of the circles μ, ν and γ , therefore it lies
on the radical axis of μ and ν .

Since the radical axis of two intersecting circles passes
through their points of intersection, the given problem is
reduced to the preceding one - that of finding the points
of intersection of a circle (μ or ν) with a straight line
(*FG*).

16. RULER CONSTRUCTIONS, GIVEN THE CENTRE OF A CIRCLE AND ITS ARC

Suppose we are given a straight line π in the plane α (we shall call it the <u>basic straight line</u>), and a point P not on the line in the same plane (<u>the basic point</u>). We shall investigate the following transformation of the plane α. The point P and every point of the straight line π transform into themselves. Any other point M of the plane α transforms into a point N, the fourth harmonic point of $P, Q; M$, where Q is the point of intersection of the straight lines π and PM (Fig. 58). Hence it follows directly that the point N transforms into M, that is, points M and N interchange places; indeed, from the equation $(PQMN) = -1$, and from Theorem 8 we obtain: $(PQNM) = -1$, therefore M is the fourth harmonic point to $P, Q; N$.

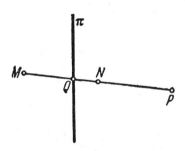

Fig. 58

The transformation described above will be called by us the <u>harmonic transformation</u> of a plane. We now note some of its properties.

It is easily seen that a straight line passing through P transforms into itself. Furthermore, the straight line m, not passing through P, transforms itself into the straight line n, which can be constructed thus. If m and π intersect at a point S and a point M on n, other than S, transforms

itself into the point N then the straight line n is drawn
through S and N (Fig. 59). Indeed, on the basis of Theorem
6, any point M' of the straight line m, transforms itself
into the point of intersection of PM' and SN.

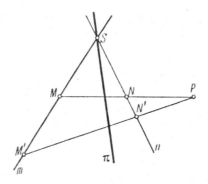

Fig. 59

If S is a point at infinity, then n, m, π are parallel.
If m is a straight line at infinity, then n bisects the segments joining the point P with points on the straight line
π .

If P is the pole of the straight line π with respect to a
conic section q , then q transforms into itself and the points
of intersection of the curve q with the straight line passing
through P interchange places. This fact is a corollary of the
polar properties of conic sections (Section 9).

Problem 32. The arc AB and the centre K of a circle $\varkappa$ is
sketched in. Construct the points of intersection of the
circle $\varkappa$ with a given straight line m .

Firstly, we shall note, that at a given or constructed
point H of the circle $\varkappa$ (on the arc or outside of it) it is
possible to construct a tangent to $\varkappa$, using a ruler alone
(Problem 7). If an arbitrary straight line is drawn through
H , then it is possible to draw the second point of intersection of this straight line with the circle $\varkappa$ (Problem 8).
Indeed, the circle $\varkappa$ is a conic section, and on its arc AB
it is possible to take as many points as necessary for the
solution of the problems indicated.

Let us tackle the solution of the problem set.

We draw the straight line AB and construct its pole P with respect to the circle $\varkappa$, as the point of intersection of tangents to $\varkappa$ at A and B (Fig. 60). We shall suppose that the straight line m has no points in common with the given arc AB and that it intersects the straight line AB produced at the point S .

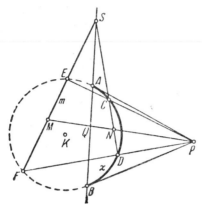

Fig. 60

We take any point M on m , other than S , and we draw the straight line PM. Let it intersect the straight line AB at the point Q . We construct the point N , the fourth harmonic point to $P, Q; M$, and we construct the straight line SN . Let this straight line intersect the given arc AB at points C and D , and the straight lines PC and PD intersect m at points E and F . These points are the required points of intersection of the circle $\varkappa$ and the straight line m .

Indeed, taking the point P and the straight line AB as the basic point and straight line and applying the harmonic transformation to the figure constructed, we note that the circle $\varkappa$ transforms into itself, and the straight lines m and SN interchange places, therefore also their points of intersection with the circle $\varkappa$ interchange places.

The investigation of Problem 32 leads us to the conclusion that every constructive problem of the second degree can be solved by means of a ruler, if the centre and an arc of a

certain circle x are sketched in in the plane of the construction, since in this case it is also possible, using the ruler
alone, to find the points of intersection of the circle x
with any secant straight line, and subsequently, to carry out
all the construction of Section 15.

The first to come to this conclusion (independently of each
other) were the Italian mathematician Severi and the Soviet
mathematician D.D. Mordukhai-Boltovskoy*.

---

*Dmitrii Dmitriyevich Mordukhai-Boltovskoy (1876-1952) is
known for his investigations in the sphere of geometry and the
history of mathematics. He laid down the fundamentals of
the systematic development of the theory of geometric constructions in Lobachevskii space.

17. THE CONSTRUCTION, BY MEANS OF A RULER, OF CIRCLES BELONGING TO A GIVEN COAXIAL SYSTEM

We discuss two preliminary auxiliary propositions.

T h e o r e m 21. If the straight line PK, where K is the centre of the circle $\varkappa$, intersects the polar π of the point P with respect to $\varkappa$ at the point P', then the points P and P' are inverse with respect to the circle $\varkappa$.

Let us denote the points of intersection of the straight line PK with the circle $\varkappa$ by M and N, and let us construct the point Q, inverse to P with respect to $\varkappa$. It follows from Theorem 11 that the points $P, Q; M, N$ form a harmonic range. Therefore, the points P' and Q coincide, which is the required result.

T h e o r e m 22. If a system of coaxial circles and a point P in its plane is given, then the polars of this point with respect to all the circles of the system are concurrent at the point Q and the mid-point of the segment PQ lies on the radical axis of the system.

Let us consider three circles of the given coaxial system λ, μ, ν, with centres L, M, N and the point P, not lying on the straight line LM (Fig. 61).

Let the polars l and m of the point P with respect to λ and μ intersect at the point Q. Let us construct a circle ω, using the segment PQ as diameter. It will pass through the point of intersection L' of the mutually perpendicular straight lines l and PL, and through the point of intersection M' of the mutually perpendicular straight lines m and PM.

The points P and L' are inverse with respect to μ (Theorem 21); therefore on the strength of Theorem 1 the circle ω is orthogonal to the circles λ and μ. Accordingly it is orthogonal also to the circle ν and its centre O lies on the radical axis of the system.

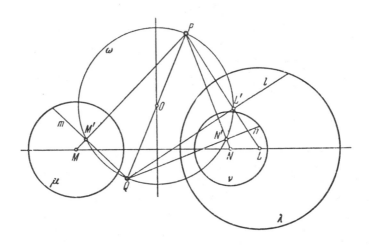

Fig. 61

Let us construct the straight line PN and let us denote
the second point of its intersection with the circle ω by
N'. The polar n of the point P with respect to the circle
ν passes through N' (from the orthogonality of circles ν and
ω)and is perpendicular to the straight line PN. But
$\angle PN'Q = 90°$ since it is subtended by a semicircle of ω and
so the straight line $N'Q$ is the polar of P with respect to
the circle ν. Hence the theorem is valid.

If the point P lies on the line of centres of the coaxial
system, then its polars with respect to the circles λ, μ and
ν are parallel. In this case the point Q is a point at infinity and the points P and Q do not define a segment.

It follows from Theorem 16 that the polars of point Q with
respect to the circles of the given system pass through the
point P. The points P and Q are called polar conjugates.
Let us consider that circle of the coaxial system, that passes
through the point P. The polar of point P with respect to
that circle is the tangent to it at P. On the basis of
Theorem 22, it passes through Q. In the same way we make
sure that the straight line PQ touches that circle of the
system which passes through Q. Thus, the straight line PQ
is the common tangent of the two circles mentioned.

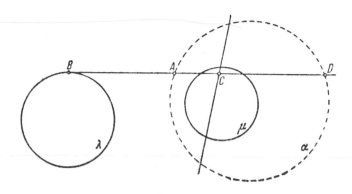

Fig. 62

Problem 33. <u>Construct five points of a circle ɑ , passing through a given point A and belonging to a system of coaxial circles given by the sketched-in circles λ and ɥ .</u>

Let the point A lie outside at least one of the given circles, for example, outside the circle λ (Fig. 62).

Let us draw a tangent AB , through A to λ , touching λ at B (see Problem 5). We construct the point C, polar conjugate of B (it lies on the straight line AB) and the point D , the fourth harmonic point of B, C, A .

The point D lies on the circle ɑ . This follows from the definition of a polar and from the fact that the polar of B with respect to ɑ , passes, on the basis of Theorem 22, through the point C .

The construction can be continued taking D as the point of departure. Indeed, the point D lies on the tangent to the circle λ , therefore it lies outside this circle. If D coincides with A , then, in order to construct a point distinct from A , belonging to the circle ɑ , it is possible to make use of a second tangent drawn from A to λ .

If we have five points of a circle ɑ or three points and tangents at two of them (for example, AE and DF , where E and F are points, which are polar conjugates of A and D respectively) then the construction of new points of this circle can be carried out without the use of circles λ and ɥ (see

Section 12).

Now, let us examine the case, when the point A lies inside both circles λ and μ (Fig. 63).

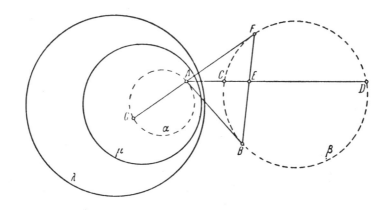

Fig. 63

We construct the point B , polar conjugate of A . It lies outside the circles λ and μ , subsequently, it is possible to construct any number of points of a circle β , belonging to the given system and passing through B . The straight line AB will be the common tangent of circles α and β .

Through the point C of the circle β , other than B , we draw the straight line AC , we find the point D at which AC cuts the circle β for the second time, and the point E , the fourth harmonic point of $C, D; A$. The straight line BE is the polar of the point A with respect to β . We construct the second point (F) of intersection of this straight line with the circle β . Then it is possible to construct on the straight line AF , tangent to circle β , a point G of the circle α , other than A , as was shown above.

Similarly it is possible to draw a tangent to β from G , distinct from GF and to find a third point of the circle α . Continuing the construction, we find the fourth point of this circle, after which it is possible to find new points of the circle, without the use of λ and μ (see Problem 10).

18   ON THE IMPOSSIBILITY OF CONSTRUCTING THE CENTRE
      OF A CIRCLE BY MEANS OF A RULER

   In Section 15 we considered ruler constructions on condition, that, in the plane of construction, there exists a
sketched-in circle of known centre. In this connexion, the
question naturally arises; is it possible, using the ruler
alone, to construct the centre of the drawn circle, if that
centre is not given? This construction is carried out easily,
if, for instance, there is a drawing of a parallelogram or of
another circle and its centre in the plane of construction.
But in the case when we do not have the use of these or any
other auxiliary figures, it is impossible to solve the problem set, as follows from Theorem 23, demonstrated below.
Let us consider two circles, which have no points in common,
μ and ν , whose centres are M and N (Fig. 64). Let their
radical axis intersect the straight line MN at the point O .

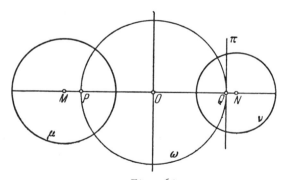

Fig. 64

We describe the circle ω with centre O , orthogonal to the
given circles. Let it intersect the straight line MN at
the points P and Q . Let us draw a perpendicular at Q to
MN. The points P and Q are symmetrical both with respect
to μ and with respect to ν (Theorem 2). Therefore, from
Theorems 11 and 14, the point P is the pole of the straight
line π with respect to each of the circles μ and ν .

Let us apply to the constructed figure the harmonic transformation, taking P and π for the basic point and straight line (see Section 16). Then the circles μ and ν transform into themselves, but their centres, lying outside the segment PQ transform into points lying inside this segment. This circumstance will be made use of in proving Theorem 23.

T h e o r e m   23. If two given non-concentric circles μ and ν have no points in common, then it is impossible to construct their centres M and N, using ruler alone.

If this construction is possible, then it will be carried out as follows; we select several arbitrary points in the plane of circles μ and ν , and we draw several arbitrary straight lines, then we construct straight lines passing through the selected points and through the points in which the straight lines, constructed previously, intersect each other and with the given circles, finally, we find the centre of one of the given circles, as the point of intersection of two definite straight lines from among the ones constructed.

If we apply the harmonic transformation considered above to the figure obtained as a result of this construction, we obtain a new figure, which can be formed by repeating exactly all constructions carried out in finding the centre of one of the given circles. The only difference will consist of the fact that the arbitrarily chosen straight lines and points will be different than the ones in the first figure. Therefore the new construction is fully equivalent to the first one, since each of them can be started merely by constructing arbitrary points and drawing arbitrary straight lines.

If our supposition is correct each of the two considered constructions should therefore bring us in the same way, to the finding of the centre of the same circle. But this is impossible, since as a result of the harmonic transformation the centres M and N of circles μ and ν transform into points other than M and N subsequently, the straight lines, which intersected at the centre of circle μ (or ν) in the first construction, transform into straight lines, whose point of intersection does not lie in the centre of this circle. Thus, the supposition about the possibility of constructing the centre of the circle μ or ν by means of a ruler is incorrect.

Therefore it is also impossible to construct the centre of a circle by means of a ruler, if only this circle is drawn.

The proof demonstrated above applies also in the case when several non-concentric circles are described, all belonging to one hyperbolic coaxial system. If, for example, the system is defined by circles μ and ν , then the application of the same harmonic transformation proves this proposition.

19. CASES, WHEN IT IS POSSIBLE TO CONSTRUCT THE
CENTRES OF TWO DRAWN CIRCLES BY MEANS OF A RULER

For the following, it is important to note that it is possible to draw by means of a ruler, a diameter of a drawn
circle if two parallel lines (p and q) are drawn in its
plane. If they intersect the given circle, we carry out the
construction indicated in Fig. 65. The straight line AB is
the required diameter. In other cases we arrive at the same
configuration by making use of the fact that it is possible
to draw a straight line parallel to the straight lines p and
q through any point on the given circle (Problem 15). Hence
it follows that it is possible to construct by means of the
ruler two diameters of the drawn circle, and that means, its
centre, if a parallelogram is drawn in its plane.

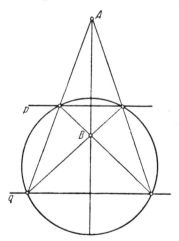

Fig. 65

Problem 34. Construct by means of a ruler the centres of
two drawn circles λ and μ in each of the following cases.

78

1. Apart from the given circles, a pair of parallel straight lines, p and q are drawn in their plane.

2. The given circles intersect.

3. The given circles touch each other.

4. The given circles are concentric, but their common centre is unknown.

5. The given circles are non-concentric and have no common points. The point A on their radical axis is known.

6. The given circles are non-concentric and have no common points. The point A on their line of centres is known.

We shall discuss each of the enumerated cases separately.

The straight lines, marked in by a pointed line in the drawings, are not constructed. They are needed for the justification of the constructions.

1. We construct poles P, Q of straight lines p and q with respect to λ and the poles P', Q' of the same straight lines with respect to μ (Fig. 66).

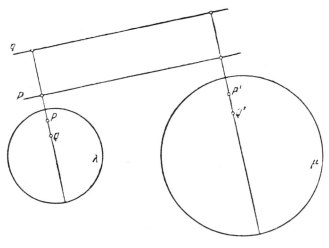

Fig. 66

The straight lines p, q, PQ and $P'Q'$ form a rectangle, since PQ is perpendicular to p, and $P'Q'$ to p.

If the straight line $P'Q'$ coincides with PQ, it will be the
line of centres of the given circles. In this case the method
of construction indicated above is useless, but we can use the
construction in 6.

2. F i r s t   s o l u t i o n. We take any two points
C and D on one of the given circles, other than their points
of intersection and we carry out the construction indicated
in Fig. 67. The straight lines EH and GF are parallel since
$\angle 1 = \angle 2 = \angle 3 = \angle 4 = \angle 5 = \angle 6$. We then construct in a similar way two more parallel straight lines and we obtain a paral-
lelogram.

S e c o n d   s o l u t i o n. At the point B of intersection of the given circles we draw a tangent BC to the
circle λ we take any point D on λ and we construct the straight
lines DA, DB, CE (Fig. 68). Then $\angle 1 = \angle 2 = \angle 3$, therefore
CE is parallel to DB .

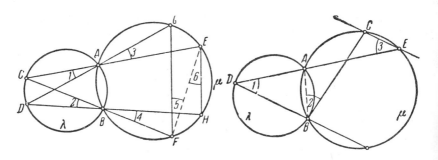

Fig. 67   Fig. 68

Note that the problem can be solved by these methods also
when one of these circles is not fully drawn. It is sufficient to have five of its points which must include the two
points of intersection of the given circles.

3. The construction of two parallel straight lines BC and
DE is shown in Fig. 69 where $\angle 1 = \angle 2 = \angle 3 = \angle 4$.

4. We carry out the construction shown in Fig. 70 and we
obtain the two parallel straight lines AB and CD .

5. We construct the point B , polar conjugate of point

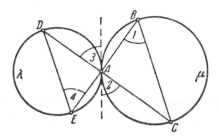

Fig. 69

A on the radical axis. The straight line AB is the radical axis of the given circles. We take a point C outside the straight line AB and we construct the point D, the polar conjugate of C. The straight line AB bisects the segment CD (Theorem 22) therefore it is possible to draw a straight line parallel to CD (Problem 13) and make use of construction 1. If the point A lies both on the radical axis and the line of centres of circles λ and μ, then the radical axis is parallel to the polars of point A with respect to λ and μ.

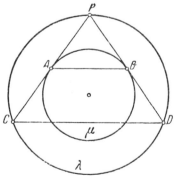

Fig. 70

6. Having constructed the polars of point A with respect

to the circles λ and μ , we draw the line of centres AB of these circles (compare Fig. 65).

We take any point C on the circle λ not lying on the straight line AB (Fig. 71) we construct the point D , the polar conjugate of C and five points of circle γ which passes through D and belongs to the coaxial system definable by the circles λ and μ (Problem 33).

The straight line CD is the common tangent of circles λ and γ, subsequently, its point of intersection E with the straight line AB is the centre of similitude of these circles. We take any point F on γ and we draw the straight line EF . Let it intersect the circle λ at points H, K and let it intersect the circle γ for the second time at the point G . Then DF is parallel to CH and DG to CK .

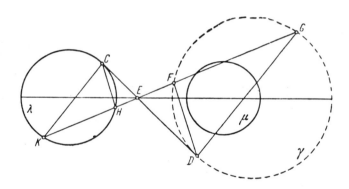

Fig. 71

20. ON THE CONSTRUCTION BY MEANS OF A RULER OF THE CENTRES OF SEVERAL CIRCLES

Problem 35. Four circles have been drawn ϰ. λ, μ and ν and no three of them belong to the same coaxial system. Construct the centre of one of these circles by means of a ruler.

We shall suppose that among the given circles there are no concentric ones or any having common points, since in the opposite case we could make use of constructions 2, 3 or 4 of Problem 34.

The essence of the solution consists of the construction of an auxiliary circle intersecting one of the given circles, and both points of intersection should be known. After that the construction 2 of Problem 34 is used.

We take any point A on the circle ϰ and we construct four more points of the circle ϰ passing through A and belonging to the coaxial system (λ. μ)* and four more points of the circle β passing through A and belonging to the system (μ, ν) (Fig. 72).

In as much as the second point of intersection of circles ϰ and α (ϰ and β) is unknown, it is necessary to construct one more auxiliary circle in such a way that it should be easy to find both points of its intersection with circle ϰ . For that, we take a point B on α inside the circle ϰ and we draw a tangent BC to α (C lies on ϰ).

Note that the point B can be taken outside of the circle ϰ , as long as the tangent at B to the circle α intersects the circle ϰ .

Let us denote by γ the circle passing through the point C and belonging to the system (α, β) .

We construct the points F and D, polar conjugates of B and

---

*This is the way we shall denote the system defined by circles λ and μ .

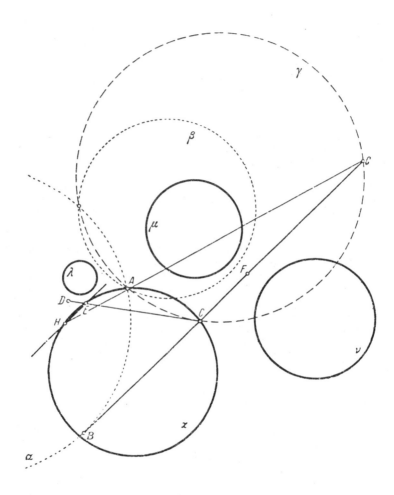

Fig. 72

C with respect to the circles of the system $(\alpha, \quad \beta)$, the
point G - the fourth harmonic point to the points B, F; C ,
- and the straight line AG.

The point G lies on the circle γ and the straight line CD
touches γ at C (see Section 17). The point A also lies

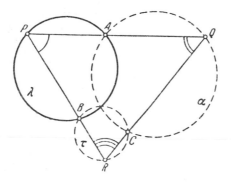

Fig. 73

on the circle γ , since γ passes through the points of intersection of circles α and β . Thus, two points, A and C ,
common to the circles κ and γ are known.

Let the straight lines CD and AG intersect the circle γ for
the second time at the points E and H . Then EH is parallel
to BC (see the second solution of Problem 34, 2). Further
we make use of the construction 1 of Problem 34.

The solution considered is useful also in the case when one
of the circles λ, μ or ν is given by five points.

Problem 36. Construct by means of a ruler the centre of
one of three drawn circles λ, μ and ν , not belonging to the
same coaxial system.

We shall assume that no two of the given circles have any
points in common or a common centre.

We take any point A on λ and we construct the points of a
circle α , passing through A and belonging to the coaxial
system (μ, ν) .

We further draw a variable straight line through A . We
denote its other point of intersection with λ by P , and
with the circle α by Q (Fig. 73). If we fix the positions
of the points B and C other than A , on the circles λ and
α respectively, then the point of intersection R of the

straight lines *BP* and *CQ* will describe the circle τ if the
straight line *PQ* is made to rotate about the point *A* . It
is easy to make sure of that by considering the sizes of the
angles of triangle *PQR* , therefore it is easy to construct
five points of the circle τ .

No three of the circles λ, μ, ν, τ belong to one coaxial system*.

Therefore it is possible further to use the construction
in Problem 35.

---

*The circle τ does not belong to the hyperbolic coaxial sys-
tem (μ, ν) since it intersects the circle α of this system. The
circle μ (and in the same way, the circle ν) do not belong to
the elliptical coaxial system (λ, τ) since it does not intersect
the circle λ .